THE STONE MOVED
Prophet Muhammad for Little Hearts

By
SANIYASNAIN KHAN

Goodwordkidz
Helping you build a family of faith

The Prophet Muhammad ﷺ once told a story of how three men, out for a walk in the mountains, were caught in a rainstorm. They quickly took shelter in a cave, but the entrance to it was at once blocked by a huge stone which came hurtling down the mountain side.

2

Now it was impossible for them to get out. So they began to pray to Allah, recalling the good deeds they had done, in the hopes that Allah would be pleased with them and set them free.

The first one said that he and his wife and children were living with his aged parents. Whenever he returned with his herd, he milked the animals and then offered the milk first to his parents and then to his children.

6

One day, he went far away and, by the time he came back home, it was very late and his parents had fallen asleep. He milked the herd as usual and brought the milk to his parents, but seeing that they were sound asleep, he did not feel like waking them up.

His children ran to him for their milk, but he felt it was not right to give it to them before he gave it to his parents. So he stood there all night, waiting for his parents to get up. They did not awaken till the break of dawn. Only then, when they had had their milk, did he give any to his children.

What he did that day had been done to please Allah, and he begged his Maker, if He had seen any virtue in his behaviour, to set them free. Miraculously, the stone moved a little bit, but not enough to let them out.

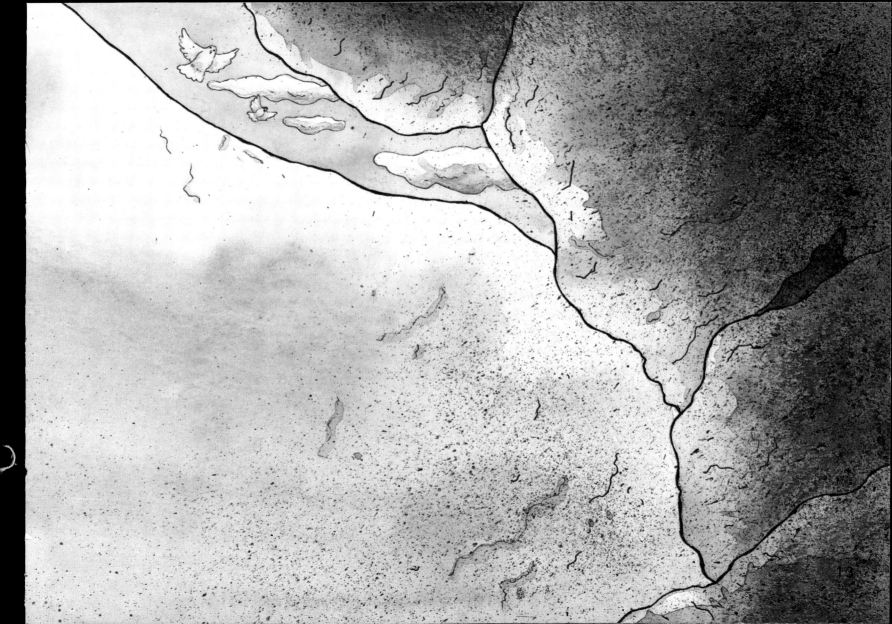

The second man said that he had a
cousin with whom he was very much
in love and whom he was very keen to
marry. But she refused to marry him
and stayed away from him.

Then a time came when she was in dire need of help, because of a famine that year. She came to him and he gave her 120 gold coins. Then he wanted to marry her forcibly, but she pleaded with him not to do so. He agreed to her request and, turning away from her, he allowed her to go away and take the gold coins with her.

The man begged Allah to remember
that he had done this out of fear for
Him, and beseeched Him to help them.
So the stone moved another little bit,
but the gap was still not wide enough
for them to come out of the cave.

18

The third man said that once he had hired the services of a workman for a bushel of rice. When the work was completed, he gave the man his bushel of rice, but the workman, not liking the quality of it, went off without it.

So he kept re-planting it until he had earned enough money
from its sale to buy some cows. Years later, the workman returned
and demanded his wages. He told the man to take away the cows
which had greatly multiplied by that time. And this he promptly
did without leaving a single cow for their owner.

22

After telling this tale, he begged
Allah to release them, as he had
done this good deed for fear of Him.
So the stone moved a little more
and made a big enough gap for
them to come out of the cave.